A Note from Levi's Mo

The message of "I Love You More than Me" is deeper than it may appear at first glance. To anyone reading this story to the students in their classroom or to their own children at home, thank you for taking the time to talk about and recognize the importance of acceptance and unconditional love.

Levi was born with both 9p deletion and Trisomy 21 syndrome. Nobody in the medical field knew what to expect for his quality of life, and honestly, the bar was initially set pretty low. But as Levi grew and developed, one thing became apparent; he has a capacity to love others that runs deep. Despite his developmental delays, cognitive impairments, and physical limitations, his ability to love others far exceeds what most of us are capable of on our own.
Levi and Norah's real-life friendship is just one example of the special bond he forms with others. So, when Clayton, Norah's daddy decided to write a children's book about their sweet friendship, we were all for it! Then we read what he wrote and realized it was more than just a cute rhyming story about two kids and a race.

You see, Norah's acceptance of who Levi is is reflected in her daddy's words. For one, the story is written from Levi's perspective, with typical thoughts, words, and emotions, much like our own. His actual physical limitations are not highlighted in the book because they don't matter. Levi is not defined by what he can or cannot do. To Levi's family and friends who know and love him, he is just Levi; a little boy who shows us how to be more concerned with others' happiness rather than our own, and who displays an amazing amount of empathy for others. A little boy whose very existence seems to emulate God's example of unconditional love as his every hug seems to say, "I love you more than me".

One sunny morning,
Levi woke to say,
"Today's the best time
to go outside and play"

I Love You More Than Me

By Clayton Martin

Illustrated By Zak Tracy

This book is dedicated
to my family. I love you
more than me.

Looking out the window
and across the street,
Levi saw Norah
getting ready for her meet.

He ran out of his room with a smile on his face, in hopes to help Norah get ready for her race.

A whistle around his neck
and his shoes tied tight,
he dashed through the door
with all of his might.

He crossed the road
after looking both ways,
because he knows to be safe
before he plays.

They head to the line
and get ready to run,
as their joy is beaming
as bright as the sun.

Levi blows the whistle
to start the race,
and off they go,
at a very fast pace.

When all of a sudden, Norah trips to the ground and the smile on her face turns upside down.

Without running ahead
or skipping a beat,
Levi reaches his hand
and helps Norah to her feet.

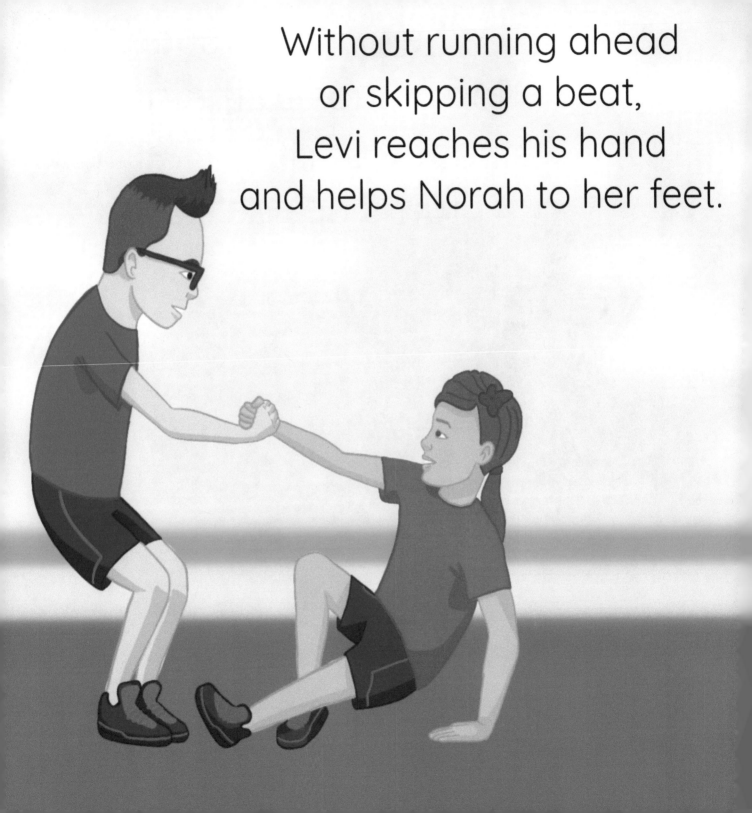

Together they head
towards the finish line,
as a pair of friends
To make each other shine.

As they smile
and as they cry,
Levi says to Norah
without being shy...

"No matter the day,
I hope that you see
I'll always show you,
I love you more than me."

About Author and Illustrator

Clayton Martin

This is the very first book that Clayton has published and wouldn't want it to be anything else. He and his family live in Birmingham, AL where his two little girls run the world. Norah, the girl character in this book, has the most compassionate heart and he is so excited to continue to watch her grow. Clayton is already working on more ideas to further share the message of love, friendship, and hope for the world.

Zak Tracy

Zak was very excited and honored to be the artist that Clayton chose to illustrate his first book. He is a young artist that lives in Tampa, FL, where he is running a small art business, called Zak Tracy Art. Zak hopes to be able to illustrate more books in the future and share more of his art with the world.

CPSIA information can be obtained
at www.ICGtesting.com
Printed in the USA
LVHW071924141021
700312LV00009B/59